LIVING on the EDGE

Dare to Experience True Spirituality

A proven pathway to become like Jesus

are you **r12?**

Being a genuine disciple of Christ flows out of relationship with Him.
It's about experiencing God's grace, not earning His love through performance.
Romans chapter 12 provides a relational profile of an authentic disciple.
Christians who live out this kind of lifestyle are what we call r12 Christians....

- **surrendered** to God
- **separate** from the world
- **sober** in self assessment
- **serving** in love
- **supernaturally** responding
  to evil with good

God is willing to go deeper and
grow you into a real disciple.
Are you ready?

r12 resources designed to help individuals, small groups, and local churches grow as disciples of Jesus Christ include...

r12 media resources
- dvd series
- cd series
- study guide

the r12 online experience...FREE!
- video Q&A
- life coaching
- interactive study guide
- online journal
- leader resources

to get r12 resources or learn more, go to LivingontheEdge.org today!

table of contents

ρ12

becoming a Romans 12 Christian

a word from Chip Ingram

We are all spiritual. Whether we embrace it or run from it, God has hard-wired spirituality into our DNA. We are living in a time where there is much intrigue and interest surrounding spiritual realities. Believers and non-believers alike are looking for ways to find spiritual meaning in their lives.

It is not enough for us to search for spirituality, we must pursue TRUE spirituality. Yet, for many of us who are Christ-followers, true spirituality seems elusive. Many believers describe their Christian life as "stuck" and "not working" in spite of all the books, seminars, church programs and religious activity. We know that something is wrong and that God has more for us than what we are experiencing.

This series is a starting place in beginning to define what an authentic disciple looks like in the 21st century. The goal of this series is to strip away all the clutter and help us rediscover the essence of the Christian life. During these 10 sessions we will take a journey together to answer the question "What is a disciple?".

Romans 12 provides us a clear picture of an authentic follower of Christ. This one chapter is Paul's executive summary of a disciple. The Bible has a lot to say on this topic, but this is a great place to begin.

I am excited that you and your group are joining me on this journey. I really believe that these weeks together will bring TRUE spirituality into focus and help your next steps in being an authentic Christ follower.

Let's get started!

Teaching Pastor, Living on the Edge

how to get the most out of this experience

Your group is about to begin what could be a life-changing journey. This powerful study of Romans 12 with Chip Ingram provides breakthrough teaching about what it means to be an authentic follower of Jesus Christ. Listed below are the segments that are part of each week's lesson as well as some hints for getting the most out of this experience. If you are leading the group, you will find additional help and coaching starting on page 60.

TAKE IT IN

During this section you will watch the teaching video. Chip will introduce each session with a personal word to the group. Next, the group will watch the teaching section. At the end of this segment, Chip will wrap up the session and help the group begin discussion. A teaching outline with fill-in-the-blank exercises is provided for each session. As you follow along, remember to write down questions or insights that you can share during the discussion time. Even though most of the verses will appear on the screen and in your notes, it is a great idea to bring a Bible each week. It will allow you to make notes in your Bible and find other passages that might be relevant to that week's study.

TALK IT OVER

Discussion questions are provided so your group can further engage the teaching content. Keep the following guidelines in mind for having a healthy group conversation.

- **Be involved.** Jump in and share your thoughts. Your ideas are important. You have a perspective that is unique and can benefit the other group members.
- **Be a good listener.** Value what others are sharing. Try to really understand the perspective of others in your group and don't be afraid to ask follow up questions.
- **Be courteous.** Always treat others with the utmost respect. When there is disagreement, focus on the issue and never turn the discussion into a personal attack.
- **Be focused.** Stay on topic. Help the group explore the subject at hand and try to save unrelated questions or stories for afterwards.
- **Be careful not to dominate the conversation.** Be aware of the amount of talking you are doing in proportion to the rest of the group and allow others to speak, too.
- **Be a learner.** Remain sensitive to what God might want to teach you through the lesson, as well as through what others have to say.

LIVE IT OUT

These simple suggestions help the lesson come to life. Don't ignore them; give them a try! Check in with another group member during the week and ask how it's going.

DIVE DEEPER

Often, these sessions can raise as many questions as they answer. From our years of experience in working with Christians and small groups, we have tried to anticipate some of those questions. In your study guide at the end of each session, you will find a few common questions about that week's topic or passage. Chip has videotaped brief answers to these questions and they are available online. All you need to do is to go to **LivingontheEdge.org** to access this helpful resource.

true spirituality™

SESSION 1

God's dream for your life

Just like we have dreams for our kids, God has a dream for His children. More than God's dream being about what we do or the kind of job we have, His dream is about the kind of person we will become. But what kind of person does He want us to become? We could spend a lot of time offering our opinions and ideas or we could let God speak for Himself. In this opening session, Chip gives us an overview of an authentic Christ-follower that comes straight from the Scripture. Let the journey begin.

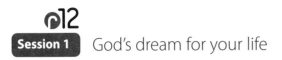

TAKE IT IN (WATCH THE VIDEO)

Every parent has a dream for their _____.

Our kids can be a source of great _____ or immeasurable _____.

Your heavenly Father has a _____ for you.

The LORD your God is with you, He is mighty to save. He will take great delight in you,
He will quiet you with His love. He will rejoice over you with singing.
Zephaniah 3:17 (NIV)

God's big agenda:

Developing your _____ and making you like His Son.

MORE IMPORTANT THAN WHAT YOU DO
IS WHAT YOU BECOME.

A Christ-follower (disciple) is not defined by

- _____

- _____

Romans 12 – The executive summary of an authentic Christ-follower.

GOD'S DREAM IS THAT 'CHRISTIANS' WOULD ACTUALLY LIVE LIKE CHRISTIANS.

• Your relationship with _____…Surrendered to God (v.1)

• Your relationship with the _____…Separate from the world (v.2)

• Your relationship with _____…Sober in self-assessment (v.3-8)

• Your relationship with _____…Serving in love (v.9-13)

• Your relationship to _____…Supernaturally responding to evil with good (v.14-21)

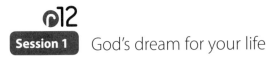

 **TALK IT OVER**

1. When you were growing up, what did it mean to be a good Christian?

2. Chip talked about God being a heavenly Father who has a dream for us. As you were growing up, what was your view of God?

   What was He like?

   How has your understanding of God changed?

3. In your opinion, why are so many Christians stuck and not growing spiritually?

4. How is spiritual maturity defined in your church?

   If you were trying to describe the road to spiritual maturity to a brand new Christian, how would you describe it?

5. Over the course of your Christian life, who or what has had the most impact on your spiritual growth?

6. How would you describe your spiritual growth over the last 5 years? When did you grow the most?

7. How satisfied are you with your spiritual health?

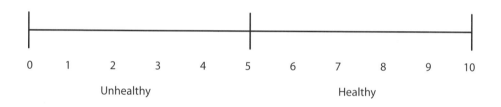

0   1   2   3   4   5   6   7   8   9   10

Unhealthy   Healthy

LIVE IT OUT

1. Read Romans 12 every day this week. This can be done in less than 5 minutes each day.

2. Commit to participating in this group for all 10 sessions.

true spirituality™

SESSION 2

how to give God what He wants the most

Therefore, I urge you, brothers, in view of God's mercy,
to offer your bodies as living sacrifices, holy and
pleasing to God-- this is your spiritual
act of worship.
Romans 12:1 (NIV)

If you could sit down with God and ask Him the question: 'What do you want from me?' What do you think He would say? If we could really know what God expects from us, maybe we could live with greater purpose and priority. Would He talk about keeping rules, following rituals, or practicing religion? We might be surprised at His answer.

TAKE IT IN (WATCH THE VIDEO)
A breakthrough question…

"God, if You do exist, what do You want from me?"

Case Study #1: John's Civil War coins

Case Study #2: Sheila's Picasso
For this to be a good decision:

Their discovery would have to be _____.

They would need _____ others didn't have.

They would need _____ to risk making the decision.

Case Study #3: Ancient Treasure

The kingdom of heaven is like a treasure hidden in the field, which a man found and hid again; and from joy over it he goes and sells all that he has and buys that field. Again, the kingdom of heaven is like a merchant seeking fine pearls, and upon finding one pearl of great value, he went and sold all that he had and bought it." Matthew 13:44-46 (NASB)

Thesis = _____ is the channel through which God's best and biggest blessings flow.

THE NATURE OF SURRENDER IS 'ALL OR NOTHING'

Definition: "Total commitment is the alignment of one's motives, resources, priorities, and goals to fulfill a specific mission, accomplish a specific task, or follow a specific person" – Webster's Dictionary

NEGATIVE	VS.	POSITIVE
Sacrifice		Joyful Wise
Self-denial		Logical
Noble, More Spiritual, Martyr		True Shrewd
Renunciation		**Re-evaluation**

The Problem = Lack of _____
The Answer = Romans 12:1

Therefore, I urge you, brothers, in view of God's mercy, to offer your bodies as living sacrifices, holy and pleasing to God— this is your spiritual act of worship.
Romans 12:1 (NIV)

The Command = "_____ your bodies"
This is not about salvation. This is about surrender (Lordship).

The Motivation = "the _____ of God"

The Reason = "spiritual act of _____"

GOD'S POWER DOESN'T KICK IN UNTIL LORDSHIP KICKS IN

Session 2 how to give God what He wants the most

What Does God Want Most? He wants _____!

A check graphic:

	1025
	DATE _____
PAY TO THE ORDER OF *Jesus Christ*	$ *100%*
All I Am and All I Have ------------------- DOLLARS	
SIGN HERE	
MEMO _____	
⑆000000000⑆ ⑆000000000⑆ ⑈1025	

For the Lord God is a sun and shield; The Lord will give grace and glory; No good thing will He withhold from those who walk uprightly. Psalm 84:11 (NKJV)

The Surrender Question = Are you all in?

TALK IT OVER

1. What is your biggest barrier to *complete surrender*? Is there anything that keeps you from saying "I'm all in"? Or for those of you who *are* all in, what was the number one fear that kept you from surrendering to Christ?

2. We can look at *surrender* through either a positive or negative lens. Which lens do you tend to look through? How does your view of God square with the following quote from A.W. Tozer: "*The whole outlook of mankind might be changed if we could all believe that we dwell under a friendly sky and that the God of heaven, though exalted in power and majesty, is eager to be friends with us.*"

3. Chip said "total commitment is the channel through which God's best and biggest blessings flow"…what are some ways in which you have experienced this to be true in your life?

4. Read 1 Corinthians 6:19-20. If you were to really be *all in*, how would your life be different this next month?

5. Who is the most committed Christ-follower you know?
   What is it about their life that is different?

6. Paul says that the motivation for our surrender is God's mercy (His grace, acceptance, forgiveness and love). In other words, in light of all that God has done for us, surrender is reasonable. Spend a few moments sharing how God's mercy has changed your life.

 **LIVE IT OUT**

1. Every day this week pray this simple prayer;
   "Lord, help me see you as you really are."

2. Sometime during this week, write out a prayer of surrender.
   Set aside enough time to carefully consider your prayer of surrender.
   In your own words, let God know that you are *all in*.

3. Take the next step and share your prayer of surrender with a friend or fellow group member.

DIVE DEEPER

• Go to www.LivingontheEdge.org/r12 to watch Chip answer these frequently asked questions.

• I know and feel that I should follow through and make that decision to *surrender* to God, but, for some reason I just can't bring myself to that level of commitment. What is the danger to me if I don't make that commitment?

• If I make the decision to surrender, I know it will affect my life and I will lose some of my friends. They won't like me or want to be with me anymore. What can I do to avoiding losing them?

• Can you tell me if a person that is not fully surrendered to Christ is a Christian or not?

true spirituality™

SESSION 3

how to get God's best for your life

part 1

Do not conform any longer to the pattern of this world, but be transformed by the renewing of your mind. Then you will be able to test and approve what God's will is-- His good, pleasing and perfect will.
Romans 12:2 (NIV)

There is a world system that threatens God's dream for your life. This world system is subtle, seductive, and orchestrated by none other than Satan himself. And none of us are exempt from its influence. This week's session will open your eyes to why so many Christians live defeated lives. Chip's teaching will help you know how to say "yes" to God and "no" to the world system. It is the only way to get God's best for your life.

TAKE IT IN (WATCH THE VIDEO)

WHY ARE THERE SO MANY DECISIONS AND SO FEW DISCIPLES?

1. Negative Command:
"Do not be conformed to the pattern of this world…"
Romans 12:2

Do not be conformed = do not be squeezed into the world's _____ .

• The world system is orchestrated by _____ .

• The world system is a _____ .

Transition: Stop allowing yourselves to be molded by the influences and pressures of this present world system.

Do not love the world nor the things in the world. If anyone loves the world, the love of the Father is not in him. For all that is in the world, **the lust of the flesh** *and the* **lust of the eyes** *and the* **boastful pride of life,** *is not from the Father, but is from the world. The world is passing away and also its lusts; but the one who does the will of God lives forever.*
1 John 2:15-17 (NASB)

• Lust of the flesh = passion to _____ (pleasure)

• Lust of the eyes = passion to _____ (possessions)

• Boastful pride of life = passion to _____ (position)

The problem: Our diet is of the world instead of the _____ .

2. Positive Command:
"…but be transformed by the renewing of your mind."
Romans 12:2

SPIRITUAL METAMORPHOSIS IS AN INSIDE JOB

Metamorphosis = change from the _____

Transformation begins when you start putting the word of God in your _____ .

Translation: But allow God to completely change your *inward thinking* and *outward behavior* by cooperating wholeheartedly moment-by-moment with the Spirit's renewing presence.

 **TALK IT OVER**

1. Where do you battle the most? Where is the world system squeezing you?

2. What are some values of the world system that are contrary to God's values?

3. Read John 17:13-18. What does it mean to be *in* the world, but not *of* the world?

What are some things we readily accept today as believers that would have been unthinkable 25 years ago?

How do you feel about some of these changes?

4. Share a time in your personal journey when the Christian life and living for God was a real battle.

How did you get through it?

What did you learn?

5. I John 2:15-17 describes 3 areas of common temptation.

Lust of the flesh = passion to feel (pleasure)
Lust of the eyes = passion to have (possessions)
Pride of life = passion to be (position)

Which of these 3 is the greatest temptation for you?

6. What one practical change could you make in the next couple of weeks that would help you say "no" to the world system? Write it out below.

_____

_____

_____

_____

LIVE IT OUT

1. Do a 48 hour media fast. Ask a friend or family member to do this with you. Commit to pray for one another and to hold each other accountable. Consider having your entire group do this together this next week.

2. Have a discussion with your family or with a good friend about this week's session. Spend some time talking about the impact of media on our lives and how we should respond as followers of Christ.

3. Spend some time in prayer this week, ask God to help you have a spiritual breakthrough to answer question #6.

SHARE YOUR STORY

In the Bible, the people of God often kept a record of God's activity. If God is using this series to have an impact on your life in some specific way, share your story at **LivingontheEdge.org**. Just click on the *Share Your Story* tab to get started.

DIVE DEEPER

- Go to www.LivingontheEdge.org/r12 to watch Chip answer these frequently asked questions.

- I live a life that I think is separate from the world and am more active than many of my friends in my church, but I still feel a sense of emptiness. Why do I feel so empty?

- My spouse is living a worldly life and I feel constantly drawn into it. What should I do?

- How do I face and deal with the "private" sins of my life? Can I keep them to myself?

true spirituality™

SESSION 4

how to get God's best for your life

part 2

Do not conform any longer to the pattern of this world, but be transformed by the renewing of your mind. Then you will be able to test and approve what God's will is-- His good, pleasing and perfect will.
Romans 12:2 (NIV)

Part of *becoming* like Christ is learning to *think* like Christ. That doesn't come easy or natural for us. The gravitational pull in our lives is to buy into the world's values and beliefs. But here's the great news—we can break free and be transformed in our thinking. This week we will discover the process God wants to use to bring about our transformation.

 **TAKE IT IN (WATCH THE VIDEO)**

The _____ **of Transformation**

_____ _____ _____

> *But we all, with unveiled face, beholding as in a mirror the glory of the Lord, are being transformed into the same image from glory to glory, just as from the Lord, the Spirit.*
> 2 Corinthians 3:18 (NASB)

The Means of Transformation

3 Keys to Renewing the Mind

• Refocus on _____…Surrender

• Recognize that the mind is a _____ .

> *For the weapons of our warfare are not carnal but mighty in God for pulling down strongholds, casting down arguments and every high thing that exalts itself against the knowledge of God, bringing every thought into captivity to the obedience of Christ.*
> 2 Corinthians 10:4-5 (NKJV)

YOU ARE WHAT YOU EAT— BOTH PHYSICALLY AND SPIRITUALLY

• Renewal of the mind is a _____ work of the Spirit.

The Practical Steps of Transformation

1. _____ **God's Word**

> *Consequently, faith comes from hearing the message, and the message is heard through the word of Christ.*
> Romans 10:17 (NIV)

2. _____ **God's Word**

> *Blessed is the one who reads the words of this prophecy, and blessed are those who hear it and take to heart what is written in it, because the time is near.*
> Revelation 1:3 (NIV)

3. _____ **God's Word**

> *Do your best to present yourself to God as one approved, a workman who does not need to be ashamed and who correctly handles the word of truth.*
> 2 Timothy 2:15 (NIV)

4. _____ **God's Word**

> *How can a young man keep his way pure? By living according to your word. I have hidden your word in my heart that I might not sin against you.*
> Psalm 119:9,11 (NIV)

5. _____ **on God's Word**

> *Do not let this Book of the Law depart from your mouth; meditate on it day and night, so that you may be careful to do everything written in it. Then you will be prosperous and successful.*
> Joshua 1:8 (NIV)

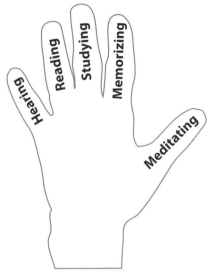

Getting a Grasp on God's Word

GOD IS AND HE HAS SPOKEN...THROUGH SCRIPTURE

The Purpose of Transformation

"To get God's best so that you may test (by experience) what God's will is…"

- **Good:** winsome, attractive, beautiful, richly satisfying
- **Pleasing:** acceptable to God and pleasing to us
- **Perfect:** according to design; maximizing our fullest potential in fulfilling God's purpose for our lives

Resources from Living on the Edge to Help You Apply Romans 12:2
- *Ancient Paths to Intimacy with God*
- *The Miracle of Life Change*
- Visit **LivingontheEdge.org/r12**

 **TALK IT OVER**

1. What specific practices have been most helpful in renewing your mind?

2. Chip said "You are what you eat physically and you are what you eat spiritually. And the greatest crime happening in the spiritual body today is an entire generation, young, medium and old that are filling their minds with trivia and media and junk, and the world system." How do you respond to his statement?

3. What is the biggest hindrance to you spending time in God's word on a regular basis?

4. Psalm 19:8 (NLT) says *The commandments of the LORD are right, bringing joy to the heart. The commands of the LORD are clear, giving insight to life.* Share a personal example of how the word of God has given you insight into some life situation.

5. Which of the five areas is the one you need to work on over the next few weeks? Hear, read, study, memorize, or meditate. Share with the group what you will do this next week.

6. Share a verse or passage of Scripture that is especially meaningful to you and why this Scripture has special significance in your life.

LIVE IT OUT

1. 3-4 times this next week commit to spend at least 15 minutes with God's word.

2. Memorize one verse this week and share it with at least one person in your group.

3. This week, pray for the others in your group by name. Ask God to give them discipline to spend time with His word. This is a list of suggestions:
   Psalm 119:105
   Philippians 4:13
   Matthew 22:36-37
   Galatians 2:20

DIVE DEEPER

- Go to www.LivingontheEdge.org/r12 to watch Chip answer these frequently asked questions.

- I'm not regularly reading my Bible. Does God look down on me if I don't have a healthy devotional life?

- I'm constantly drawn into my kid's life and constantly ruled by their schedule. How should I protect myself from all the busyness?

- I don't know how to read the Bible. How do I start reading it?

true spirituality™

how to come to grips with the real you

part 1

For by the grace given me I say to every one of you:
Do not think of yourself more highly than you ought,
but rather think of yourself with sober judgment,
in accordance with the measure of faith God has given you.
Just as each of us has one body with many members,
and these members do not all have the same function,
so in Christ we who are many form one body,
and each member belongs to all the others.
We have different gifts, according to the grace given us.
If a man's gift is prophesying, let him use it in proportion to his faith.
If it is serving, let him serve; if it is teaching, let him teach;
if it is encouraging, let him encourage;
if it is contributing to the needs of others, let him give generously;
if it is leadership, let him govern diligently;
if it is showing mercy, let him do it cheerfully.
Romans 12:3-8 (NIV)

Who are you? That question can be answered in so many ways. It can be answered with "I'm John Smith", or "I'm an electrician", or "I'm a mother", or "I'm a surfer". While all of those answers might define something about us, they don't really define who we are at the core of our being. They don't really drill down to the level of true identity. During our session today, Chip is going to drill beneath the surface and talk about the relationship you spend the most time with—your relationship with YOURSELF.

TAKE IT IN (WATCH THE VIDEO)

One of your most significant relationships is with _____ .

> # ONE OF YOUR GREATEST DAYS
> # IS THE DAY YOU DISCOVER WHO YOU ARE.

3 Questions We All Ask Ourselves

1. _____ am I? (Identity)

2. Where do I _____? (Security)

3. What am I supposed _____? (Significance)

Why is it so Hard to Answer These Questions?

They heard the sound of the LORD God walking in the garden in the cool of the day, and the man and his wife hid themselves from the presence of the LORD God among the trees of the garden.

Then the LORD God called to the man, and said to him, "Where are you?"

He said, "I heard the sound of You in the garden, and I was afraid because I was naked; so I hid myself."

And He said, "Who told you that you were naked? Have you eaten from the tree of which I commanded you not to eat?"

The man said, "The woman whom You gave to be with me, she gave me from the tree, and I ate."

Then the LORD God said to the woman, "What is this you have done?" And the woman said, "The serpent deceived me, and I ate."
Genesis 3:8-13 (NASB)

EVER SINCE THE GARDEN WE'VE BEEN HIDING FROM GOD AND FROM OTHERS.

3 Implications for How We See Ourselves

1. Fear rooted in _____. I'm afraid.

2. Hiding rooted in _____. I don't want to be seen.

3. Blaming rooted in _____. I'm a victim.

   Each one of us struggles with _____.

   We cover our insecurities with _____ reactions or _____ reactions.

   The key is learning to _____ who God made you to be.

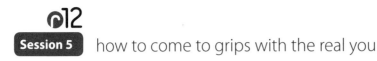

Session 5   how to come to grips with the real you   part 1

TALK IT OVER

1. Growing up, what did you do to overcome your insecurity and get others' approval?

2. When you were growing up, who was your hero?

   Who did you want to be like?

3. What were the primary messages you received from your parents that have shaped your view of yourself?

4. Describe a time when you were trying to *belong*.

5. When did you have the greatest sense of belonging in your life?

6. Ephesians 2:10 (NLT) says *For we are God's masterpiece. He has created us anew in Christ Jesus, so that we can do the good things He planned for us long ago.* Honesty is important with this next question. How well do you accept how God made you and who He made you to be?

7. Spend some time affirming one another. As you think about others in your group, complete the following statement. "One of the things I appreciate about you most is…"

LIVE IT OUT

1. Read Psalm 139:1-18 every day this week. Read the verses slowly and let them sink into your spirit. Try reading the passage out loud and every time you read a personal pronoun, say your own name.

2. Make a list this week of statements that are true about your identity. Spend some time with your Bible seeking to discover what God says about you. Start with Romans 8 and Ephesians 1.

DIVE DEEPER

• Why is it important to have a *sober assessment* of myself? Will it really make a difference?

• I'm a Christian, but how do I know if the Spirit of God is in my life even though there are things in my life that aren't good?

• Important people in my life are putting me down. How do I deal with this?

true spirituality™

SESSION 6

how to come to grips with the real you

part 2

For by the grace given me I say to every one of you:
Do not think of yourself more highly than you ought,
but rather think of yourself with sober judgment,
in accordance with the measure of faith God has given you.
Just as each of us has one body with many members,
and these members do not all have the same function,
so in Christ we who are many form one body,
and each member belongs to all the others.
We have different gifts, according to the grace given us.
If a man's gift is prophesying, let him use it in proportion
to his faith.
If it is serving, let him serve; if it is teaching, let him teach;
if it is encouraging, let him encourage;
if it is contributing to the needs of others, let him give generously;
if it is leadership, let him govern diligently;
if it is showing mercy, let him do it cheerfully.
Romans 12:3-8 (NIV)

Have you ever wondered why God didn't take you to heaven
at the moment of your conversion. He certainly could have.
So, why did He leave you here? He left you here because He has
an assignment for you. You have a role to play, something to
contribute to God's work on this earth. This session will help you
discover where you fit, why you need other people, and what
God has uniquely shaped you to do.

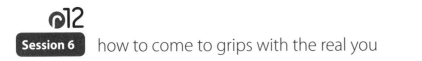

how to come to grips with the real you part 2

 **TAKE IT IN** (WATCH THE VIDEO)

Answering 3 of Life's Most Important Questions

1. _____ **are you?**

> *For by the grace given me I say to every one of you: Do not think of yourself more highly than you ought, but rather think of yourself with sober judgment, in accordance with the measure of faith God has given you.*
> Romans 12:3

You are commanded to think _____ about yourself.
Not too high (pride)
Not too low (inferiority)
Genuine humility = not thinking of yourself _____

2. **Where do you** _____?
> *Just as each of us has one body with many members, and these members do not all have the same function, so in Christ we who are many form one body, and each member belongs to all the others.*
> Romans 12:4–5

You belong in the body of Christ because you have a _____ .

WE LITERALLY, PHYSICALLY, TANGIBLY ARE THE BODY OF CHRIST.

3. **What are you supposed** _____?

> *We have different gifts, according to the grace given us. If a man's gift is prophesying, let him use it in proportion to his faith. If it is serving, let him serve; if it is teaching, let him teach; if it is encouraging, let him encourage; if it is contributing to the needs of others, let him give generously; if it is leadership, let him govern diligently; if it is showing mercy, let him do it cheerfully.*
> Romans 12:6–8

Discover and deploy your _____ .

Never Forget Who You Really Are!

1. God created you to be completely unique.

You are eternally _____ (Psalm 139:13-14)

GOD NOT ONLY LOVES YOU, HE EVEN LIKES YOU.

2. God placed you in His family.

You are unconditionally _____ (Ephesians 3:19-21)

3. God gave you certain gifts to fulfill His purpose.

You are uniquely _____ (Ephesians 2:10)

 RESOURCES

From Living on the Edge to Help You Apply Romans 12:3-8
Your Divine Design
Living Without Hypocrisy
For Women: *Precious in His Sight,* Theresa Ingram
LivingontheEdge.org/r12

Session 6   how to come to grips with the real you   part 2

 **TALK IT OVER**

1. Use a 3x5 card or use the space provided in your study guide. Write down 3 things you are good at and 3 things at which you are not so good. Once this is written, share one thing from each of the 2 categories with the group.

THINGS I AM GOOD AT

1. _____

2. _____

3. _____

THINGS I AM NOT GOOD AT

1. _____

2. _____

3. _____

2. What is the most significant thing you have learned about yourself in the last 5 years?

3. Have someone read aloud 1 Corinthians 12:14-26. Where do you fit in the body of Christ? How connected do you feel within the body of Christ? What could help you feel more connected?

4. What is your primary spiritual gift? Where do you love to serve? (Where do you feel effective and fulfilled when you serve)?

5. Do you feel like you are fully using your spiritual gift? If not, what is standing in the way?

6. If time and money were not an issue, what would you attempt for God?

7. Which of the following 3 statements do you find the most difficult to believe and accept about yourself? Why?

    • You are eternally valuable.

    • You are unconditionally accepted.

    • You are uniquely significant.

LIVE IT OUT

1. Make it your mission this week to help people know how they were wonderfully created. Look for opportunities all week long to say to people "I'm really glad God made you just the way He did… you are a gift to me." If you are a parent, make it a special point to do this with your kids.

2. If you are struggling to know your gifts, try this little exercise. Do a little informal survey of people that know you well. Ask them this simple question; "Based on what I'm good at and passionate about, how could you see God using me to serve others?" The answer to this question will tell you a lot about the gifts God bestowed on you.

3. If God is doing something in your life through this study, we would like you to share it. Go to the Living on the Edge website (**LivingontheEdge.org**) and click on the Share Your Story tab. What God is doing in you will be an encouragement to others.

DIVE DEEPER

•   Go to www.LivingontheEdge.org/r12 to watch Chip answer these frequently asked questions.

•   I think I know my spiritual gift, but I haven't been successful in using it. What should I do?

•   Can I only use my spiritual gift in my church?

•   There are a lot of people in my church with similar spiritual gifts. How should I plug in somewhere without compromising my gifts?

true spirituality™

SESSION 7

how to experience authentic community

part 1

Let love be without hypocrisy.
Abhor what is evil; cling to what is good.
Be devoted to one another in brotherly love;
give preference to one another in honor;
not lagging behind in diligence, fervent
in spirit, serving the Lord; rejoicing in hope,
persevering in tribulation, devoted to prayer,
contributing to the needs of the saints,
practicing hospitality.
Romans 12:9-13 (NASB)

The Bible knows nothing of *Lone Ranger Christianity.*
Scripture says that we all *belong* to one another. In other
words, you need a heart connection with a few other
believers where you find support, love, encouragement,
accountability, prayer and friendship. So often as
believers we only relate to each other at a surface
level. This session will help you pursue authentic, life-
affirming community.

TAKE IT IN (WATCH THE VIDEO)

When you are going to die,
you tell people the things that are absolutely most _____ to you.

A Command to His Followers

A new command I give you: Love one another. As I have loved you, so you must love one another.
By this all men will know that you are my disciples, if you love one another.
John 13:34-35 (NIV)

The greatest apologetic in the world is Christians _____ Christians.

A Prayer for His Followers

My prayer is not for them alone. I pray also for those who will believe in me through their message,
that all of them may be one, Father, just as you are in me and I am in you.

May they also be in us so that the world may believe that you have sent me. I have given them the
glory that you gave me, that they may be one as we are one: I in them and you in me.

May they be brought to complete unity to let the world know that you sent me and have loved them
even as you have loved me.

Father, I want those you have given me to be with me where I am, and to see my glory, the glory you
have given me because you loved me before the creation of the world.
John 17:20-24 (NIV)

> **JOHN 17 IS THE ONE TIME IN THE BIBLE THAT**
> **JESUS PRAYED FOR YOU SPECIFICALLY.**

Authentic Community Occurs When...
>   The real you... (v.9)
>   meets real needs... (v.10)
>   for the right reasons... (v.11)
>   in the right way (v.12-13).

The Real You Should Be Characterized By...

_____ – "Let love be sincere."

_____ – "Hate what is evil. Cling to what is good."

At the heart of true community is _____.

THE VERY FIRST SIN OF THE NEW TESTAMENT CHURCH WAS DISHONESTY.

Without _____ the command of John 13 and the prayer of John 17 would never become a reality.

 **TALK IT OVER**

(Consider breaking up into groups of 3-4 for the discussion time)

1. Describe a time when you were around someone with whom you felt really free to be yourself.

2. Describe the closest friendship you ever had and what made that friendship so special.

3. Chip talks about authenticity and honesty as characteristics of true community. What other characteristics would you use to define true biblical community (fellowship)? What are some things that can prevent true fellowship from happening in your life, in your small group, and even in your church?

4. Romans 12:5 says we "belong to one another" and Romans 12:10 says that we are to be "devoted to one another". What would it look like for your small group to live out Romans 12:5 and 12:10?

5. Share a time when you needed the support of your friends to make it through a difficult time.

6. In light of your personality and spiritual journey, how can this group best support you?

7. What is one tangible, practical way that you personally could serve your group in love?

 **LIVE IT OUT**

1. Think of a person you feel safe with and someone you'd like to get to know a little bit better. Take the initiative to get together with them.

2. This week write a letter to someone who has provided true, authentic community in your life. Tell them what their friendship has meant to you and how their life has had an impact on you.

DIVE DEEPER

- Go to www.LivingontheEdge.org/r12 to watch Chip answer these frequently asked questions.

- I want to be involved in a small group community, but I'm an introvert. What should I do to get into a community?

- How can I help my small group stop "going through the motions" and start going deeper?

- How do I know when I'm acting like a hypocrite?

- How do I deal with someone that I feel is a hypocrite?

true spirituality™

SESSION 8

how to experience authentic community

part 2

Let love be without hypocrisy.
Abhor what is evil; cling to what is good.
Be devoted to one another in brotherly love;
give preference to one another in honor;
not lagging behind in diligence, fervent
in spirit, serving the Lord; rejoicing in hope,
persevering in tribulation, devoted to prayer,
contributing to the needs of the saints,
practicing hospitality.
Romans 12:9-13 (NASB)

Serving others is inherent in authentic community.
It is not just about being supported, it is about
offering support. Community is not just about
having our needs met, but it is about meeting
the needs of others. It's messy, uncomfortable,
inconvenient, and tiring. And, yet it's worth it. You
are never more like Jesus than when you are serving.

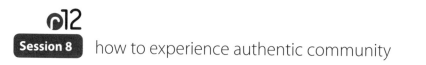
TAKE IT IN (WATCH THE VIDEO)

Authentic community is experienced when the real you...

Meets Real _____ . (v.10)

Devotion – "Be devoted to one another in brotherly love."

Be devoted = _____ love

Humility – "Giving preference to one another in honor."

Giving preference = passion for another person's success

YOU CAN IMPRESS FROM A DISTANCE, BUT YOU IMPACT BY SERVING PEOPLE UP CLOSE AND PERSONAL.

For the Right _____ (v.11)

Motive –
Not lagging behind in diligence – don't be _____ but fervent in spirit

bubbling up with _____ serving the Lord

How I respond when I am treated like a servant will reveal my true motive.

True love is choosing to give another person what they need most, when they deserve it the least, and at great personal cost.

That's how _____ loves us.

In the Right _____ (v.12-13)

_____ "Rejoicing in hope, persevering in tribulation, devoted to prayer."

_____ –"Contributing to the needs of the saints, practicing (pursuing) hospitality."

LEARN TO LOVE PEOPLE WITH
EXCELLENCE AND EXTRAVAGANCE.

What step can you take to experience authentic community?

Session 8 how to experience authentic community part 2

 TALK IT OVER

1. What's the biggest barrier that keeps the real you from meeting real needs for the right reasons in the right way?

2. How much does "busyness" impact your ability to see and meet others' needs? What would it look like for you to slow down?

3. As a group, brainstorm as many examples as possible when Jesus *noticed* and met a need.

4. Read Luke 13:10-17. In this story, what lessons can we learn from Jesus about meeting real needs for the right reason in the right way?

5. What are some signs or indicators that we are not serving for the *right reason*?

6. Paul challenges us to "contribute to the needs of the saints". The early church set a great example of sacrificial generosity. Read Acts 2:44-45 and Acts 4:32-35.
   Describe a time when someone's generosity met a *real* need in your life.

7. Paul also challenges us to practice hospitality which literally means to pursue strangers. Think of one tangible, practical way you could *practice hospitality* this week toward someone far from God.

 **LIVE IT OUT**

1. Decide upon a need that you could meet as a group. Put together a plan so that sometime in the next month your group can practice *radical generosity*.

2. This week personally do something that anonymously blesses someone in need.

DIVE DEEPER

- Go to www.LivingontheEdge.org/r12 to watch Chip answer these frequently asked questions.

- I have a leadership position in the church but I'm finding it harder and harder to serve others. Why is that?

- I'm burned out from serving in my church, but I'm afraid that everything will fall apart if I stop serving. What should I do? Can I take a break?

- What is the value of serving in community rather than just serving on my own?

RESOURCES
From Living on the Edge to help you apply Romans 12:9-13
- *Love One Another*
- *Five Lies That Ruin Relationships*
- **LivingontheEdge.org/r12**

true spirituality™

SESSION 9

how to overcome
the evil aimed at you

part 1

Bless those who persecute you; bless and do not curse.
Rejoice with those who rejoice; mourn with those who mourn.
Live in harmony with one another.
Do not be proud, but be willing to associate with people of low position.
Do not be conceited. Do not repay anyone evil for evil.
Be careful to do what is right in the eyes of everybody.
If it is possible, as far as it depends on you, live at peace with everyone.
Do not take revenge, my friends, but leave room for God's wrath,
for it is written: "It is mine to avenge; I will repay," says the Lord.
On the contrary: "If your enemy is hungry, feed him;
if he is thirsty, give him something to drink. In doing this,
you will heap burning coals on his head."
Do not be overcome by evil, but overcome evil with good.
Romans 12:14-21 (NIV)

God hard-wired into your DNA a profound ability to love deeply
and to hurt deeply. One of the risks of relationships is that we
can be seriously wounded. We all know people that are carrying
painful scars from a relational wound that happened years ago. The
question is "How do I get past the hurt"? Well, that's exactly what this
session is about.

TAKE IT IN (WATCH THE VIDEO)

How does an authentic follower of Christ respond to those who have hurt them the _____?

> *"You have heard that it was said, 'Love your neighbor and hate your enemy.' But I tell you: Love your enemies and pray for those who persecute you, that you may be sons of your Father in heaven."*
>
> *He causes His sun to rise on the evil and the good, and sends rain on the righteous and the unrighteous.*
>
> *If you love those who love you, what reward will you get? Are not even the tax collectors doing that? And if you greet only your brothers, what are you doing more than others? Do not even pagans do that? Be perfect, therefore, as your heavenly Father is perfect.*
> Matthew 5:43-48 (NIV)

BECOMING A R12 CHRISTIAN IS NOT DIFFICULT — IT IS IMPOSSIBLE.

Characteristics of a R12 Christian

It's about a _____ response, not performance

It's about _____, not rules or religious activity

It's about _____

- Loving God through a surrendered life.
- Refusing to love the world's false promises.
- Loving ourselves for who God made us to be.
- Loving fellow believers through sacrificial service.
- Loving our enemies by supernaturally returning good for evil.

A Romans 12 response to personal attack _____ to *bless* those who have
wounded you (v.14-16)

1. Forgiveness (v.14)

Forgiveness is a _____
Forgive
Forgiving
Forgiven

2. Identification (v.15)

TALK IT OVER

1. Perhaps today's teaching has brought to the surface a painful situation you are facing
   right now. Don't be afraid to ask your group for prayer. You don't have to share the details,
   but you need the prayer and support of Christian friends.

   Spend whatever time is necessary to pray for those in your group who are dealing with
   relational wounds.

2. Share about a time when you had to forgive someone who hurt you.
   How did you come to the place where you could forgive?

3. Have someone read Matthew 18:21-35. At the end of the story, the man who refused to forgive was handed over to be *tortured*.
How is refusing to forgive like handing ourselves over to be tortured?

4. Ephesians 4:32 (NLT) says "Instead, be kind to each other, tenderhearted, forgiving one another, just as God through Christ has forgiven you."
Spend some time in prayer praising God for the forgiveness we have in Jesus.

LIVE IT OUT

1. Get alone with God and make a list of all the specific things this person did to hurt or wound you. Then, this week, go through your list and one by one choose to forgive that person for these hurts.

2. Memorize Colossians 3:13 this week and try to meditate on it each day.

You must make allowance for each other's faults and forgive the person who offends you. Remember, the Lord forgave you, so you must forgive others.
Colossians 3:13 (NLT)

3. Just go to **LivingontheEdge.org** and click on the story tab to share with us how God is working in your life.

DIVE DEEPER

- Go to www.LivingontheEdge.org/r12 to watch Chip answer these frequently asked questions.

- What are some practical ways that I can bless those that have been my enemies?

- What will happen if I just avoid any conflict or hatred that I might have against someone?

true spirituality™

SESSION 10

how to overcome
the evil aimed at you

part 2

Bless those who persecute you; bless and do not curse.
Rejoice with those who rejoice; mourn with those who mourn.
Live in harmony with one another.
Do not be proud, but be willing to associate with people of low position.
Do not be conceited. Do not repay anyone evil for evil.
Be careful to do what is right in the eyes of everybody.
If it is possible, as far as it depends on you, live at peace with everyone.
Do not take revenge, my friends, but leave room for God's wrath,
for it is written: "It is mine to avenge; I will repay," says the Lord.
On the contrary: "If your enemy is hungry, feed him;
if he is thirsty, give him something to drink. In doing this,
you will heap burning coals on his head."
Do not be overcome by evil, but overcome evil with good.
Romans 12:14-21 (NIV)

Everything about this final session is counter intuitive to our human
nature. When we've been hurt, our natural response is to fight
back, get back, and pay back. Yet, God calls us to a higher standard.
If we took this teaching seriously, it could be the most difficult,
demanding, and uncomfortable thing we have ever been asked to
do. This very practical teaching will help us know how to overcome
evil with good.

TAKE IT IN (WATCH THE VIDEO)

Positive Command = Bless people
> Forgiveness (v.14)
> Identification (v.15)

> _____ (v.16)

> Ask God "Father, could you show me my part In this?" This is hard because it feels like we are letting them off the hook.

> You have a choice – _____ be God or let _____ be God

Negative Command = Don't take revenge

REVENGE IS NEVER AN OPTION FOR A FOLLOWER OF CHRIST.

> Personal retaliation is a prohibited response for God's people.
> "Be careful" = "take thought".
> Seek to understand—put yourself in their shoes.
> Everyone behaves in a way that makes sense.

> **Personal retaliation is prohibited because...**

> 1. It usurps God's role as _____ .

> 2. It is an ineffective means of _____ .

RETALIATION IS LIKE FIGHTING A FIRE WITH A HOSE FILLED WITH GAS.

You will never be more _____ than when you give evil people good.

COVENANT

LORD, TODAY I COMMIT TO BE A ROMANS 12 CHRISTIAN.

Name: _____

Date: _____

 **TALK IT OVER**

1. What would happen in your life, your group, your church, and your community if, for the next 12 months, you became Romans 12 Christians?

2. How did Jesus model the concept of overcoming evil with good in His life? In His death?

3. What are some practical ways that you can *heap burning coals* on the head of a person who has wounded you?

4. Chip made a distinction between personal attacks, and legal or civil issues. What might fall into the category of personal attack and what would fall into the category of a legal/civil issue? Read Romans 13:1-5 for further help in discussing this issue.

5. For you personally, in what way has this series changed your perspective about the Christian life? What impact will this have on how you live?

 **LIVE IT OUT**

1. Take some time this week to reflect on this series. Write out a personal, expanded version of the Romans 12 covenant.

2. Take each of the 5 areas and write out 3 statements that you want to characterize your life in that area. This is worth your time and will help crystallize your thinking. Once you have written these out, share them with someone in your group and carry them in your Bible. Review and reflect on them regularly.

Surrendered to God
Example… God, from this day forward, I am *all in.*

*   _____

*   _____

*   _____

Separate from this World's Values

• _____

• _____

• _____

Sober in Self-Assessment

• _____

• _____

• _____

Serving in Love

• _____

• _____

• _____

Supernaturally Responding to Evil with Good

• _____

• _____

• _____

 DIVE DEEPER

• Go to www.LivingontheEdge.org/r12 to watch Chip answer these frequently asked questions.

• How do I make something right with a person if the person has already died?

• I tried to reconcile with someone but each time it seems the problem escalates to a bigger problem. What should I do?

 RESOURCES

From Living on the Edge to help you apply Romans 12:14-21
• _Finding God When You Need Him the Most_
• _Overcoming Emotions That Destroy_
• **LivingontheEdge.org/r12**

leader's notes

The following are valuable resources for leaders to help facilitate group interaction and growth with r12 lessons:

- group agreement

- guidelines: how to make this a meaningful experience for your group

- session notes

- prayer & praise

- group roster

- follow-up: what's next

what's next?

If your group would like to go deeper in their understanding of one of the five relationships in Romans 12, consider one of the following studies:

SURRENDER…
God: As He Longs for You to See Him

How would you describe God? Awesome? All Powerful? Creator? While we cannot know Him exhaustively, we can know Him truly. And God longs for you to see Him as He truly is. Join Chip in this fascinating series studying the seven attributes of God.

SEPARATE FROM THE WORLD…
Miracle of Life Change

Is life change really possible? If we're honest most of us would answer, "No." You've tried numerous programs that promise big changes, but in reality, deliver very little results. You long for transformation, but don't know where to begin. There's good news for you and there is hope. Life change is possible!

SOBER IN SELF-ASSESSMENT…
Your Divine Design

Do you know how God has uniquely wired you? Every believer was created to play a strategic role in the body of Christ with the gifts God has given them. But many of today's Christians face one difficult question—how do I discover my spiritual gifts and use them effectively in my church?

SUPERNATURALLY RESPONDING TO EVIL WITH GOOD…
Invisible War

Beneath our tangible landscape lurks an invisible spiritual realm where an unseen battle rages. It's real and it's dangerous. If you're prepared to remove the blinders and gaze into the unseen world, Chip is ready to take you there.

group agreement

People come to groups with a variety of different expectations. The purpose of a group agreement is simply to make sure everyone is on the same page and that we have some common expectations. The following group agreement is a tool to help the group discuss specific guidelines together during your first meeting. Modify anything that does not work for your group, then be sure to discuss the questions at the bottom of this page. This will help you to have an even greater group experience!

WE AGREE TO THE FOLLOWING PRIORITIES

- **Take the Bible Seriously** — to seek to understand and apply God's truth in the Bible

- **Group Attendance** — to give priority to the group meeting
(Call if I am going to be absent or late.)

- **Safe Environment** — to create a safe place where people can be heard and feel loved
(no snap judgments or simple fixes)

- **Be Confidential** — to keep anything that is shared strictly confidential and within the group

- **Spiritual Health** — to give group members permission to help me live a godly, healthy spiritual life that is pleasing to God

- **Building Relationships** — to get to know the other members of the group and pray for them regularly

- **Prayer** — to regularly pray with and for each other

- **Other** _____

- **Other** _____

OUR GAME PLAN

- Will we have refreshments? _____

- What will we do about childcare? _____

- What day and time will we meet? _____

- Where will we meet? _____

- How long will we meet each week? _____

how to make this a meaningful experience for your group

BEFORE THE GROUP ARRIVES

1. Be prepared. Your personal preparation can make a huge difference in the quality of the group experience. We strongly suggest previewing both the DVD teaching program by Chip Ingram along with the accompanying parts of the study guide.

2. Pray for your group members by name. Ask God to use your time together to touch the heart of every person in your group. Expect God to challenge and change people as a result of this study.

3. Provide refreshments. There's nothing like food to help a group relax and connect with each other. For the first week, we suggest you prepare a snack, but after that, ask other group members to bring the food so that they share in the responsibilities of the group and make a commitment to return.

4. Relax. Don't try to imitate someone else's style of leading a group. Lead the group in a way that fits your style and temperament. Remember that people may feel a bit nervous showing up for a small group study, so put them at ease when they arrive. Make sure to have all the details covered prior to your group meeting, so that once people start arriving, you can focus on greeting them.

TAKE IT IN (WATCH THE VIDEO)

1. Arrange the room. Set up the chairs in the room so that everyone can see the television. It's best to arrange the room in such a way that it is conducive to discussion.

2. Get the video ready. Each video session on the DVD has 3 components. During the first 2-3 minutes, Chip introduces this week's topic. Then, the group will watch the actual teaching content that Chip taught in front of a live audience. This portion of the video is roughly 20 minutes in length. Finally, Chip will then share some closing thoughts and set up the discussion topics for your group.

3. Be sure to test your video equipment ahead of time. Practice using the equipment and make sure you have located this week's lesson on the DVD menu. The video segments flow from one right into the next. So once you start the session, you won't have to stop the video until Chip has finished his closing thoughts and prepared the group for the first discussion question.

4. Have enough materials on hand. Before you start the video, make sure everyone has their own copy of the study guide. Encourage the group to open to this week's session and follow along with the teaching.

 **TALK IT OVER**

Here are some guidelines for leading the discussion time:

1. Make this a discussion, not a lecture. Resist the temptation to do all the talking and to answer your own questions. Don't be afraid of a few moments of silence while people formulate their answers. And don't feel like you need to have all the answers. There is nothing wrong with simply responding "I don't know the answer to that, but I'll see if I can find an answer this week".

2. Encourage everyone to participate. Don't let one person dominate, but also don't pressure quieter members to speak during the first couple of sessions. After one person answers, don't immediately move on; ask what other people think, or say, "Would someone who hasn't shared like to add anything?"

3. Affirm people's participation and input. If an answer is clearly wrong, ask "What led you to that conclusion?" or ask what the rest of the group thinks. If a disagreement arises, don't be too quick to shut it down! The discussion can draw out important perspectives, and if you can't resolve it there, offer to research it further and return to the issue next week. However, if someone goes on the offensive and engages in personal attack of another person, you will need to step in as the leader. In the midst of spirited discussion, we must also remember that people are fragile and there is no place for disrespect.

4. Detour when necessary. If an important question is raised that is not in the study guide, take time to discuss it. Also, if someone shares something personal and emotional, take time for them. Stop and pray for them right then. Allow the Holy Spirit room to maneuver and follow His prompting when the discussion changes direction.

5. Form subgroups. One of the principles of small group life is "when numbers go up, sharing goes down". So, if you have a large group, sometimes you may want to split up into groups of 3-5 for discussion time. This is a great way to give everyone, even the quieter members, a chance to say something. Choose someone in the group to guide each of the smaller groups through the discussion. This involves others in the leadership of the group and provides an opportunity for training new leaders.

6. Pray. Be sensitive to the fact that some people in your group may be uncomfortable praying out loud. As a general rule, don't call on people to pray unless you have asked them ahead of time or have heard them pray in public. But this can also be a time to help people build their confidence to pray in a group. Consider having prayer times that ask people to just say a word or sentence of thanks to God.

 **LIVE IT OUT**

These simple suggestions will help you apply the lesson. Be sure and leave adequate time to talk about practical applications of the lesson. This is a great way to build group community.

Try these ideas together and hold each other accountable for completing them, then share the following week how it went.

A FINAL WORD...

Keep an eye on the clock. Be sensitive to time. Whatever is the agreed upon time commitment, try to stick with it. It is always better to finish the meeting with people wanting more rather than people walking away stressed out because the meeting went long.

 **DIVE DEEPER**

We are very excited to offer this new feature for the r12 curriculum series. This is going to be a tremendous resource for you as a group leader. From our years of experience in working with Christians and small groups, we have tried to anticipate some of the questions that people your group might ask about this topic.

Chip has videotaped brief answers to some of these common questions and they are available online. These questions will be listed in your study guide at the end of each session under the section called 'Dive Deeper'. Encourage those in your group to utilize this valuable resource. All they need to do is go to the Living on the Edge website (**LivingontheEdge.org**) to see Chip's answers.

You might even want to have a computer available at the end of the first session or two so that your group can get a feel for this resource.

session notes

SESSION 1: GOD'S DREAM FOR YOUR LIFE   PAGE 1

- Be sure to take a few moments for people to introduce themselves and get acquainted.

- Make sure everyone has a study guide and encourage people to bring their Bibles each week.

- Go over the group agreement and game plan. Also, review the 'How to Get the Most Out of This Experience' section at the front of their study guide. Do this prior to watching the video teaching.

- As a way to introduce the whole series, you might want to read to the group the page entitled 'A Word from Chip'.

- Be sensitive to the fact that being in a small group might be a new experience for some. So, let people engage and participate at a pace that is comfortable for them. Be cautious about calling on people to answer questions. Read a scripture passage or pray in front of the group.

SESSION 2: HOW TO GIVE GOD WHAT HE WANTS THE MOST   PAGE 6

- Spend a few moments at the beginning checking in with the group about last week's assignment. The group was asked to read Romans 12 each day. Without shaming or embarrassing people, find out who took on the assignment. What did they learn? What new insight did they get?

- During this session Chip will talk about surrendering to the Lordship of Christ as a *moment in time* experience. It is important to make sure people in your group understand that this is not their salvation experience. This surrender moment happens AFTER conversion and is about submitting to the Lordship of Christ in our lives.

- At the close of this week's session, Chip will challenge people in your group to write out a prayer of surrender. Encourage everyone to take this seriously and to set aside some time this week to really think this through and write out their declaration of surrender. You might want to send out an e-mail reminder during the week and ask if anyone would be willing to share their written prayer at next week's meeting.

- The first question that Chip encourages the group to discuss is "What is your biggest barrier to complete surrender?" This is an intense question and some people might be hesitant to share…especially if your group hasn't been together long. As the leader, you might want to consider leading the way sharing your personal answer to that question.

SESSION 3: HOW TO GET GOD'S BEST FOR YOUR LIFE (PART 1)   PAGE 12

- Do a check in with the group about last week's assignment which was to write out a prayer of surrender. Ask some follow up questions like "How did it feel to write down your declaration of surrender?" or "Was it difficult to put your thoughts in writing?". Then, ask if anyone would be willing to share their prayer with the group.

- If someone had to miss last week, be sure to follow up to let them know they were missed. This small gesture can mean a lot.

- During this session, Chip is going to talk about the impact of the world system on us as believers. This is a struggle for every single person sitting in your group. So, as you ask the discussion questions, don't be afraid of letting there be a few seconds of silence. Sometimes people need a few seconds to process their response and to have the courage to speak up.

- This session will probe beneath the surface and identify some of the real life battles and struggles we face living in a media-driven world. People in your group need a safe place where they can talk about their struggles and find support. This might be a good week to subgroup for the discussion time.

- This week Chip will challenge your group to try a 48 hour media fast. This might sound like a simple thing, but it can be very difficult to follow through. You might want to ask the group if they would want to consider doing the 48 hour media fast together. You could agree upon a 48 hour block of time that the whole group will fast from media. Also, you could encourage families from your group to get together one night this week instead of watching TV at home.

SESSION 4: HOW TO GET GOD'S BEST FOR YOUR LIFE (PART 2)   PAGE 18

- Start off this week's session by sharing about the 48 hour media fast. How hard was it? What did they do instead? Did it have spiritual value?

- One of the ways that you will raise the ownership level in the group is to share responsibility. When people have something they are responsible for, they will have a greater connection to the group. So, if you have not done so already, get some people to help with refreshments, taking charge of the prayer list, or planning a group social.

- This week's assignment is a 30 day challenge. Over the next month the group will be challenged to spend 15 minutes a day with God. This is a great opportunity for the group to help each other and encourage each other throughout the month. Encourage people to send out e-mail updates to the group about what they learning in their time with God.

- If this is new to some people in your group, you may want to make some practical suggestions about what portions of the Bible to read. Either the book of John or the book of Proverbs are a great place to start. The amount of Scripture people read each day isn't as important as absorbing and internalizing what they are reading.

- Another Live It Out suggestion this week is to pray for each other by name. Consider dividing the group into prayer partners. Challenge the prayer partners to pray for each other this week. Also, encourage them to check in with each other to get specific prayer requests.

SESSION 5: HOW TO COME TO GRIPS WITH THE REAL YOU (PART 1) PAGE 24

- Don't forget to check in with the group about last week's assignment to start spending daily time with God. This is the most significant spiritual habit that any Christian can build into their lives. So, encourage people to stay with it and if they missed a day or two, that's OK. Encourage them to keep at it. You might also take a moment to see if anyone wants to share about their time with God this week.

- This session will be the halfway point in the series. Take a few moments to encourage the group to continue to make the group meeting a priority. Also, this is a good time to step back and assess how the group is doing. Is everyone participating? Do people seem to be growing? Is the meeting going too long?

- The last part of the discussion time this week is dedicated to an affirmation exercise. We will ask your group to complete the following statement; "One of the things I appreciate most about you is…" This can be a very powerful and encouraging experience for your group. So, leave adequate time for this.

- The assignment for this week is to read Psalm 139:1-18 every day. So, as people are spending time with God this week, encourage them to incorporate this assignment into their time with God. To get started with this, you could take a couple of minutes to read this passage out loud to close your group time.

SESSION 6: HOW TO COME TO GRIPS WITH THE REAL YOU (PART 2) PAGE 30

- Start off your time together this week by going back to Psalm 139. One way to make this

Psalm very personal is every time you see a personal pronoun, put your name there. So, consider reading out loud to the group Psalm 139:13-18 and every time you read the word 'me' or 'I', read your name.

- During this week's session Chip will talk about taking a 3x5 card and writing out 3 things you do well and 3 things you don't do well. If you don't want to hand out 3x5 cards, there is space in your study guide for people to do this exercise. After you turn off the video, give people a few minutes to actually write this down before you jump into the discussion.

- The discussion starter that Chip sets up has to do with strengths and weaknesses. After they have written down their strengths and weaknesses, he asks people to share one thing they're good at and one thing they're not so good at. It would be a good idea if you as the leader shared first. It will model authenticity and make it easier for people to do the same.

- You will notice in the study guide this week that there is a 'Share your Story' section. We would like to hear how God is at work in your group. So, if someone in your group has a story of how this study is having an impact on their life, challenge them to go to **LivingontheEdge.org** and share that story so that others may be encouraged and blessed.

SESSION 7: HOW TO EXPERIENCE AUTHENTIC COMMUNITY (PART 1)   PAGE 36

- During this session and next week's session Chip is going to dive into the topic of authentic community. Most Christians relate to one another on a surface level. But true community involves being known and knowing others deeply. Challenge the group to go to a new level of relationship with each other. A great small group not only involves good Bible study but also involves relationships where we can be *real* with each other.

- To help deepen the relationships and give people more time to share what is really going on in their lives, you might want to break into subgroups of 3-4 for the discussion time again this week. Think about your group and who you believe would be a good facilitator. Ask them to lead the subgroups.

- As we explore biblical community, it would be good to stress critical components that encourage authentic relationships. The first is confidentiality. Stress the importance of this being a "safe place" where people can share without worrying if information will get outside the group. The second component is time together outside the group meeting. If the group really wants to go to a deeper level, they will need to start developing their friendships beyond the small group meeting.

- This week's assignment has to do with pursuing relationship. Chip is going to encourage people in the group to take the initiative to get together this week with someone they want to get to know better. Many of us have good intentions to pursue these kind of relationships, but often never get around to it. Challenge the group to take this seriously.

SESSION 8: HOW TO EXPERIENCE AUTHENTIC COMMUNITY (PART 2)   PAGE 42

- The first question this week is "What's the biggest barrier that keeps the real you from meeting real needs for the right reasons in the right way?". Chip shares that his biggest barrier is busyness. Prior to your group meeting give some thought to how busyness shows itself in your life and the lives of your group. This is such a significant issue. Make sure you give it adequate time during the discussion.

- This week your group will be challenged to consider doing some kind of ministry project in the next month. Serving together not only gives you the privilege to meet the needs of others but it also deepens the relationships of your group. Once your group has decided on a project, find someone in your group with good organizational abilities to put together the plan for the group.

- One of the best ways to build authentic community in your group is to pray for and with each other. Too often prayer is simply tacked on to the end of our group meeting when everyone is ready to get home. Talk to your group about praying for each other and this week, try to make the prayer time a meaningful part of the group experience. Get a little creative with the prayer time so your group doesn't get in a rut.

- Since this is week 8 of the series you might want to start discussing what your group will study after you complete this series. After the Session 10 notes in your study guide, you will find some small group studies that will help you take one of these 5 relationships deeper. These can be ordered through the website at **LivingontheEdge.org**.

SESSION 9: HOW TO OVERCOME THE EVIL AIMED AT YOU (PART 1)   PAGE 48

- As you start the group this week, do an update on the group serving project. If you have already completed it, spend some time debriefing and celebrating. If you haven't yet done the project, spend a few minutes making sure the plans are coming together. Also, do your best to encourage every person to participate.

prayer & praise

One of the most important things you can do in your group is to pray with and for each other. Write down each other's concerns here so you can remember to pray for these requests during the week!

Use the Follow Up box to record an answer to a prayer or to write down how you might want to follow up with the person making the request. This could be a phone call, an e-mail, or a card. Your personal concern will mean a lot!

PERSON	PRAYER REQUEST	FOLLOW UP

prayer & praise

PERSON	PRAYER REQUEST	FOLLOW UP

prayer & praise

PERSON	PRAYER REQUEST	FOLLOW UP

prayer & praise

PERSON	PRAYER REQUEST	FOLLOW UP

prayer & praise

PERSON	PRAYER REQUEST	FOLLOW UP

group roster

NAME	HOME PHONE	EMAIL
1.		
2.		
3.		
4.		
5.		
6.		
7.		
8.		
9.		
10.		
11.		
12.		

Notes

Notes

Notes

Notes

Notes

Notes

WHAT'S NEXT?

More Group Studies from Chip Ingram

NEW BIO
Quench Your Thirst for Life
5 video sessions

Cinematic story illustrates Biblical truth in this 5-part video study that unlocks the Biblical DNA for spiritual momentum by examining the questions at the heart of true spirituality.

NEW House or Home Marriage
God's Blueprint for a Great Marriage
10 video sessions

The foundational building blocks of marriage are crumbling before our eyes, and Christians aren't exempt. It's time to go back to the blueprint and examine God's plan for marriages that last for a lifetime.

NEW Good to Great in God's Eyes
10 Practices Great Christians Have in Common
10 video sessions

If you long for spiritual breakthrough, take a closer look at ten powerful practices that will rekindle a fresh infusion of faith and take you from good to great...in God's eyes.

Balancing Life's Demands
Biblical Priorities for Busy Lives
10 video sessions

Busy, tired and stressed out? Learn how to put "first things first" and find peace in the midst of pressure and adversity.

Effective Parenting in a Defective World
Raising Kids that Stand Out from the Crowd
9 video sessions

Packed with examples and advice for raising kids, this series presents Biblical principles for parenting that still work today.

Experiencing God's Dream for Your Marriage
Practical Tools for a Thriving Marriage
12 video sessions

Examine God's design for marriage and the real life tools and practices that will transform it for a lifetime.

Five Lies that Ruin Relationships
Building Truth-Based Relationships
10 video sessions

Uncover five powerful lies that wreck relationships and experience the freedom of understanding how to recognize God's truth.

The Genius of Generosity
Lessons from a Secret Pact Between Friends
4 video sessions

The smartest financial move you can make is to invest in God's Kingdom. Learn His design for wise giving and generous living.

God As He Longs for You To See Him
Getting a Right View of God
10 video sessions

A deeper look at seven attributes of God's character that will change the way you think, pray and live.

Holy Ambition
Turning God-Shaped Dreams Into Reality
7 video sessions

Do you long to turn a God-inspired dream into reality? Learn how God uses everyday believers to accomplish extraordinary things.

Invisible War
The Believer's Guide to Satan, Demons & Spiritual Warfare
8 video sessions

Are you "battle ready"? Learn how to clothe yourself with God's "spiritual armor" and be confident of victory over the enemy of your soul.

Living On The Edge
Becoming a Romans 12 Christian
10 video sessions

If God exists...what does he want from us? Discover the profile of a healthy disciple and learn how to experience God's grace.

Watch previews & order at www.LivingontheEdge.org